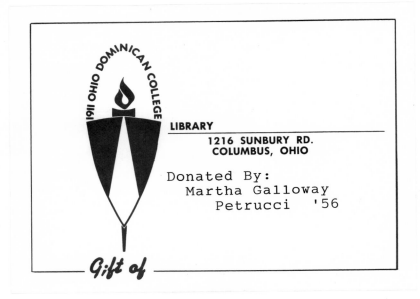

The PIED PIPER

retold in rhyme and pictures

by AL GRAHAM and TONY PALAZZO

DUELL, SLOAN AND PEARCE
New York

Affiliate of
MEREDITH PRESS
Des Moines & New York

This is the tale of a town overrun
    With rats, rats, rats;
Tale that can only be duly begun
    With "Rats! rats! rats!"
Rats by the dozen and rats by the score;
Rats of a size never sighted before;
Rats that the cats were content to ignore,
    These rats, rats, rats.

Think, sir, of being besieged and beset
    By rats, rats, rats;
Think, sir, of being beplagued and befret-
    ted by rats, rats, rats;
Rats full of mischief and rats full of spite;
Rats that would rattle you, battle you, bite;
Rats that would scare you and dare you to fight,
    The brats, brats, brats.

Think, then, of living in Hamelin town
Where swarms of the rattiest rats
Turned every trace of a smile to a frown;
Where rats...rats...rats

Gnawed into firkins of butter and cheese,
Threatened the babies with rabies disease,
Frightened the ladies at parties and teas,
And nibbled the gentlemen's spats.

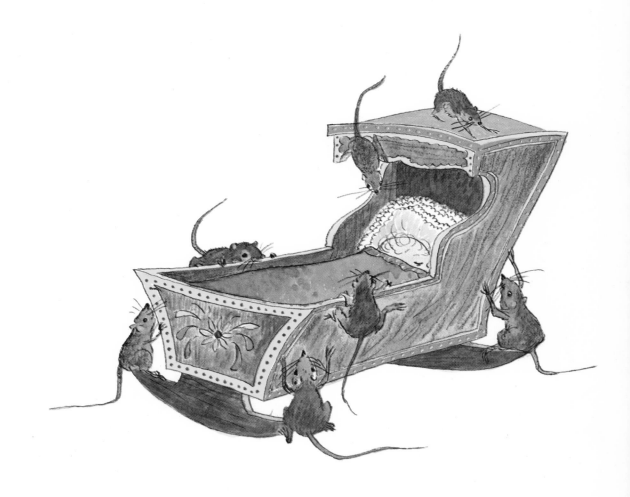

Daily the plight of the people grew worse;
    Daily the rats became tougher:
Sneakier, cheekier — daily a curse
    Tougher and tougher to suffer.
Robbing the pantries (and even the traps),
Forcing a family to feed upon scraps,
Waking the takers of afternoon naps,
    Daily the rats became tougher.

How were the people of Hamelin to quell
    Such rats, rats, rats?
Plainly, a law wouldn't curb or repel
    Such rats, rats, rats;

Poison and traps were of little avail;
Pistols were even more certain to fail;
Plainly, you couldn't imprison or jail
    Such rats, rats, rats.

Plainly, the rats had the folks in a fix:
    What were the people to do?
Wish on a star? Learn a conjurer's tricks?
    Move to Paree — or Peru?
Even the Mayor seemed rather disturbed:
"Rats, I contend, are a nuisance," he blurbed.
"Rats," he orated, "must go — or be curbed;
    Order the varmints to 'Shoo!'"

Then, as it happened, there strolled into town
  A fanciful manner of man
Wearing the pied-colored garb of a clown,
  Playing the pipe of a Pan.
Playing a tune with a fanciful beat,
Marking its rhythm with fanciful feet,
Prancing, he went, through the principal street,
  This fanciful manner of man.

Out of their holes in a spirited rush
    Came rats, rats, rats;
Out in a wild and impetuous crush
    Came rats, rats, rats;
Yea, by the dozen, the score, and the clan,
Lured by the pipe of a pied–coated Pan,
Lured by the piper, they rhumba'd and ran,
    These rats, rats, rats.

Straight went the piper (the rats at his heels),
    Straight as the word can express,
Straight amid ratty rejoicing and squeals,
    Straight to the mayor, no less.
"Greetings, Your Honor," he said with a smile;
"Pardon my following, pardon my style;
Mine is a magic, sir, mine is a wile
    Useful to those in a mess."

Mine," he continued, "yea, mine is a way
    With rats, rats, rats;
Rid you I can, sir, and rid you today
    Of rats, rats, rats;
Yea, sir, today, sir, the town can be free,
Free of its rats if you'll bargain with me:
Rid you I can — for a reasonable fee —
    Of rats, rats, rats."

Rid us, then, Piper," the mayor decreed,
"Rid us, I bid you, of rats;
Rid us (and mind you don't kid us!). Proceed!
Off with these plundering brats!

Off with these varmints with which you've a way!
Off with 'em pronto — and pronto I'll pay
Double and triple whatever you say
　　Your fee is to free us of rats."

Thus was the piper, as any can see,
   Promised his fee — and what's more,
Promised a payment that promised to be
   Triple his charge for his chore.
Wherefore, at once, without further ado,
Off went the piper, a-piping anew;
Off at his heels went his following, too—
   Rats by the dozen and score.

Promptly from hither and promptly from yon
   Came more, more rats;
Multitudes more — to be followed, anon,
   By more, more rats:
Rats that came running with kith and with kin;
Rats that were fat, sir, and rats that were thin;
Rats that could whistle and rats that could grin —
   Then more, *more* rats.

Hard on the heels of the piper they ran,
Rapt and entranced and in thrall,
Each, so to speak, sir, a Pied Piper fan
Having what's known as a ball.
Meanwhile, the piper, the fanciful chap,
Wasn't by any means having a snap:
Piping a tune to entrance and entrap
Rats isn't easy at all.

Down to the river (the rats at his heels),
    Down to its turbulent flow,
Piping, he went (to a chorus of squeals),
    Piping a chanteyman's *"Ho!..."*
Ho for the river that runs to the sea!
Ho for the river! the river for me!"
So, to the turbulent river went he,
    Piping a chanteyman's *"Ho!..."*

Hard on the heels of this fanciful man
   Came rats, rats, rats;
Down to the turbulent river they ran,
   These rats, rats, rats;
Lured by the piper a-piping them down,
Down to the river that rushed by the town,
Into the turbulent river — to *drown* —
   Plunged rats, rats, rats.

Thus was the town, as the piper foretold,
Rid of its legion of rats;
Now could its people rejoice, and (behold!)
So could its legion of cats!

Now could the piper (who'd plainly displayed
Skill beyond that of the best in his trade)
Rightly — yea, rightly — expect to be paid,
   Paid for outwitting the rats.

So, amid revelry, chanting and cheers,
  Straight to the mayor went he.
"Now, then, Your Honor," he said, "it appears
  Proper to ask for my fee."

"Fee?" said the mayor, "what fee? and for what?
Payment for piping, sir? definitely not!
Pipers, like rats, sir, are better forgot;
  Pooh, sir, for you and your fee!"

Rightly indignant, the piper (no fool)
   Rightly repressed a reply,
Rightly remained imperturbably cool . . .
Ah, but the look in his eye

Answered: "Your Honor, sir, have it your way!
Break, if you care to, your promise, I say;
Break it — but note that forever and aye,
    Ever you'll pay for your lie!"

Back to the street went the piper, and there,
  Showing no sign of his ire,
Sounded the notes of a magical air—
  Air that a Fairyland choir
Long has been known to intone to impart
Spark to the spirit and spunk to the heart,
Stirring a hope that no artist or art
  Ever can hope to inspire.

Out of the houses the girls and the boys
    Tumbled and stumbled and spilled;
Hastily leaving their games and their toys,
    They thrilled . . . thrilled . . . thrilled —
Thrilled to an air from the pipe of a Pan
Played by a fanciful manner of man;
Hard on the heels of the piper they ran,
    Bethrilled, thrilled, thrilled.

On through the market place, on through the square,
  On by the mall and the mill,
On went the piper, his magical air
  Piped with a leprechaun's skill:
"Come," it invited, "ye girls and ye boys,
Come ye to Fairyland! share ye its joys!
Share ye its toffee-tree! share ye its toys!
  Come ye to Fairyland Hill!"

Needless to tell you the children replied
  With whoops, whoops, whoops:
"Take us to Fairyland, Piper," they cried
  With whoops, whoops, whoops.
"Whoops for the piper!" they shouted with glee,
"Whoops for the toffee and whoops for the tree!
Take us to Fairyland, Piper, say we
  With whoops, whoops, whoops!"

So, with his audience skipping along,
 Gleeful, agog, and athrill,
Onward the piper went, nipping along,
 Eyes on a neighboring hill;
Eyes on a hill that impelled him to play
Strains of a melody seeming to say:
"Ho for the home of the gnome and the fay!
 Ho for their home and their hill!"

Off to the hill, to its cavernous side,
  Off with a *"Ho!"* (and a *"Hey!"*),
Blithely the children now follow their guide,
  Mindful of gnome and of fay;
Mindful of only the fun to be had
(Wholly unmindful of Mother and Dad),
Toddler and playfellow, lassie and lad,
  Mindful of gnome and of fay.

So to the foot of that cavernous hill,
   So to its cavernous base,
Now come the children, agog and athrill,
   Chorusing *"This* is the place!"
Now they behold an impassable door,
Massive, impressive, imposing — and more;
"Open it! open it, Piper!" they roar,
   "Open it! *This* is the place!"

Now, sir, this massive, impassable door,
　　Door to the heart of the hill,
Magically opens — and children aroar,
　　Gleeful, agog, and athrill,
Heeding the lead of their fanciful guide,
Follow the fanciful fellow inside,
Certain it's here that the fairies abide,
　　Here in the heart of the hill.

Now, sir, a toddler — the smallest and last —
  Enters this home of the fay;
Now, sir, the door, with a slam like a blast,
  Closes — forever and aye.

Now if you ask me, sir, "Now do they dwell,
Piper and children, in Fairyland?"...Well,
That, sir, is something the tale doesn't tell;
  That, sir, the tale doesn't say.

So ends the tale of a town overrun
    With rats, rats, rats;
So ends a curious drama begun
    By rats, rats, rats;
So ends a story of scorn and acclaim,
Magic and vengeance and villainous shame...
"Magic and vengeance — and dubious fame,"
    Say rats,

           rats,

              rats.